Contents

Introduction 4

Visors
Apple Buddy Visor 7
Pumpkin Patch Kids Visor 8
Professor Owl Visor 9
Farm Friends Visor 10

Passes 11

Stationery
Apple Buddy Stationery 12
Pumpkin Patch Kids Stationery 13
Professor Owl Stationery 14
Farm Friends Stationery 15
Notes 16

Pop-up Border
Apple Buddy Pop-up Border 17
Pumpkin Patch Kids Pop-up Border 18
Professor Owl Pop-up Border 19
Farm Friends Pop-up Border 20

Charts
Apple Buddy Chart 21
Pumpkin Patch Kids Chart 22
Professor Owl Chart 23
Farm Friends Chart 24

Tags 25

Spelling Word Pals
Apple Buddy Spelling Word Pal 26
Pumpkin Patch Kids Spelling Word Pals 27
Professor Owl Spelling Word Pal 28
Farm Friends Spelling Word Pals 29

Labels 30

Newsletters
The Apple Buddy Gazette 31
The Pumpkin Patch Kids Weekly 32
Professor Owl's News 33
Farm Friends Announce 34

Pencil Toppers ....

Book Ring Flash Cards

Doorknob Hangers
Apple Buddy Doorknob Hangers 37
Pumpkin Patch Kids Doorknob Hangers 38
Professor Owl Doorknob Hangers 39
Farm Friends Doorknob Hangers 40

Counters
Apple Buddy Counters 41
Pumpkin Patch Kids Counters 42
Professor Owl Counters 43
Farm Friends Counters 44

Clocks
Apple Buddy Clock 45
Pumpkin Patch Kids Clock 46
Professor Owl Clock 47
Farm Friends Clock 48
Clock Hands 49

Desk Plates 50

Book Report Covers
My Apple Buddy Book Report Cover 51
My Pumpkin Patch Kids Book Report Cover 52
Professor Owl's Book Report Cover 53
My Farm Friends Book Report Cover 54

Bookmarks 55

Book Plates 56

Awards
Math Awards 57
Spelling Awards 58
Science Awards 59
Reading Awards 60
Improved Awards 61
Art Awards 62
Credit Card Awards 63
Achievement Awards 64

 # Introduction

Teacher Timesavers for Fall includes everything a teacher needs to organize and manage classroom activities, communicate with parents, decorate, and develop skills practice tools. Decorate bulletin and display boards with Pop-up Borders, create a classroom newsletter, make Book Ring Flash Cards and more with the Apple Buddy, Professor Owl, Pumpkin Patch Kids, and Farm Friends patterns and forms found in *Teacher Timesavers for Fall*.

Visors Provide children with crayons or markers, scissors, glue, stapler, and oak tag strips to make visors to wear during field trips, to identify team members, helpers, or leaders. Reproduce and provide each child with a visor pattern (pp. 7-10) of his or her choice to color and cut out. Measure, cut, and staple an oak tag strip to form a headband. Help each child staple the visor pattern to his or her oak tag headband.

Staple.

Pop-up Borders Decorate bulletin and display boards with pop-up borders (pp. 17-20). Or provide children with corrugated board, construction paper, crayons or markers, scissors, glue, and four pop-up border strips to make a take-home sticky note board. Have each child glue construction paper to a sheet of corrugated board. Then have them color, cut out, trim, and glue a pop-up border strip along each edge of the board. Help children punch holes and attach yarn to hang their sticky note boards.

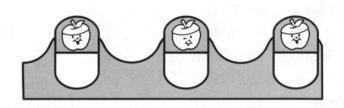

Charts Enlarge, reproduce, color, cut out, and laminate the programmable charts (pp. 21-24) to keep track of birthdays, scheduled activities, dates to remember, teams and team members, and classroom helpers. Reproduce and program smaller take-home charts to keep families informed.

Passes Reproduce and program colored construction paper passes (p. 11) for children to go to the media center, office, multipurpose room, or another classroom.

Stationery Provide children with stationery forms (pp. 12-16) to write letters to pen pals, friends, and family. Reproduce stationery notes to correspond with parents, classroom volunteers, and guest speakers.

Tags Reproduce colored construction paper tags (p. 25) or provide children with tag patterns to color and cut out. Use tags to identify team members, birthday boys and girls, helpers, and more.

Spelling Word Pals Program and reproduce spelling word pals (pp. 26-29) for children to color, cut out, and take home to study. For classroom use, reproduce and provide each child with an oak tag spelling word pal of his or her choice. Have children color their pals then laminate. Help each child cut out his or her spelling word pal. Provide children with erasable markers or crayons to write new or difficult spelling words on their pals.

Labels Label shelves, boxes, storage containers, supply cabinets, and more with the labels on page 30. Reproduce colored construction paper labels or provide children with label patterns to color and cut out. Attach labels with tape.

Newsletters Keep classroom friends, volunteers, children, and their families informed with a newsletter (pp. 31-34). Invite children to share noteworthy news. Encourage them to write articles, draw pictures or provide photographs. Share information on student achievements, improvements, birthdays, guest visitors, field trips, and more.

Pencil Toppers Reproduce oak tag or card stock pencil toppers (p. 35) for children to color and cut out. Provide crayons or markers and scissors. You may choose to provide glue and glitter. Use a craft knife to cut two slits in each child's pencil topper. Show how to slide a pencil through the slits and secure with tape. Pencil toppers also make great stick puppets.

Book Ring Flash Cards Program, then reproduce book ring flash card patterns (p. 36) with addition problems, spelling, long and short vowel words, beginning and ending sound pictures, and more. Reproduce programmed flash cards on colored construction paper or recruit volunteers to color individual cards. Laminate, cut apart, then punch a hole through each card where indicated. Thread a hinged book ring through the hole in each set of cards. book ring flash cards may be hung from cup hooks on a wall or door.

Doorknob Hangers Reproduce an oak tag or poster board doorknob hanger (pp. 37-40) for each child. Provide crayons or markers for children to color door knob hanger patterns. Laminate, then cut out each child's hanger. Provide erasable crayons or markers for children to write alternative messages on the backs of doorknob hangers.

Counters For a flannel board counting activity, glue a sheet of felt to the back of colored construction paper counter sets (pp. 41-44). Cut apart and store each set in a separate resealable plastic bag. Cover a large sheet of corrugated board with felt. Punch a hole in one corner of the board and through each plastic bag. Tie a length of yarn to each bag, then lace and tie the loose ends through the hole in the board. You may also reproduce a colored construction paper counter set for each child to use for individual counting skills practice. Laminate, then cut apart each set. Provide resealable plastic bags for children to store their counters.

Clocks Children will enjoy practicing telling time with delightful clock forms (pp. 45-49). Reproduce an oak tag clock and clock hands for each child. Provide crayons or markers for children to color clocks. Laminate, then have children cut out the clocks. Punch a hole in the center of each clock and set of hands. Use a brass fastener to attach hands to each child's clock.

Desk Plates Provide each child with the desk plate pattern (p. 50) of his or her choice. Also provide crayons or markers, scissors, and glue for children to color and cut out desk plates. Have each child write his or her name on the desk plate. Laminate, trim, and secure desks plates with removable poster adhesive.

Book Report Covers Reproduce book report cover patterns (pp. 51-54) and store each design in a separate folder. Store folders in a file box decorated with construction paper leaves. Also provide blank paper for students to trace matching report cover outlines to use as report pages.

Bookmarks Reproduce colored construction paper bookmarks (p. 55) for reading rewards. Or prepare a reward workstation with cutout bookmark patterns, crayons, markers, glue, and glitter for children to decorate individual bookmarks.

Book Plates Prepare a reading display board. Cut out and mount a large book form on the display board. Write "Books We Read" at the top of the book. Provide cutout book plates (p. 56) for children to color. Then have children write the titles of books they have read to attach to the display. Children can also use book plates to identify personal note- and story books.

Awards Reproduce colored construction paper awards (pp. 57-64) to reward students for academic achievements, improvement, and encouragement.

Apple Buddy Visor

Apple Buddy

Pumpkin Patch Kids Visor

Pumpkin Patch Buddies

Teacher Timesavers for Fall • ©2004 Monday Morning Books, Inc.

Professor Owl Visor

Farm Friends Visor

Farm Friends

Passes

 **HALL PASS**

 **VISITOR'S PASS**

 **HALL PASS**

 **VISITOR'S PASS**

 **HALL PASS**

 **VISITOR'S PASS**

 **HALL PASS**

 **VISITOR'S PASS**

Apple Buddy Stationery

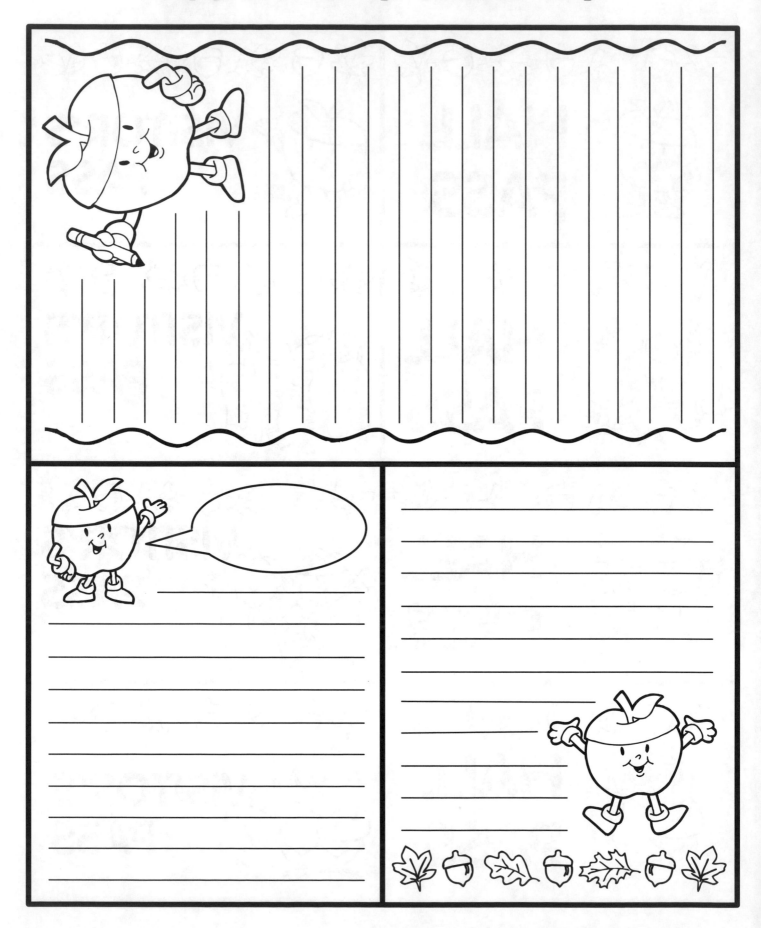

Pumpkin Patch Kids Stationery

Professor Owl Stationery

Farm Friends Stationery

Notes

Just A Little Note

Just A Little Note

Just A Little Note

Just A Little Note

Thank You!

Reminder!

Apple Buddy Pop-up Border

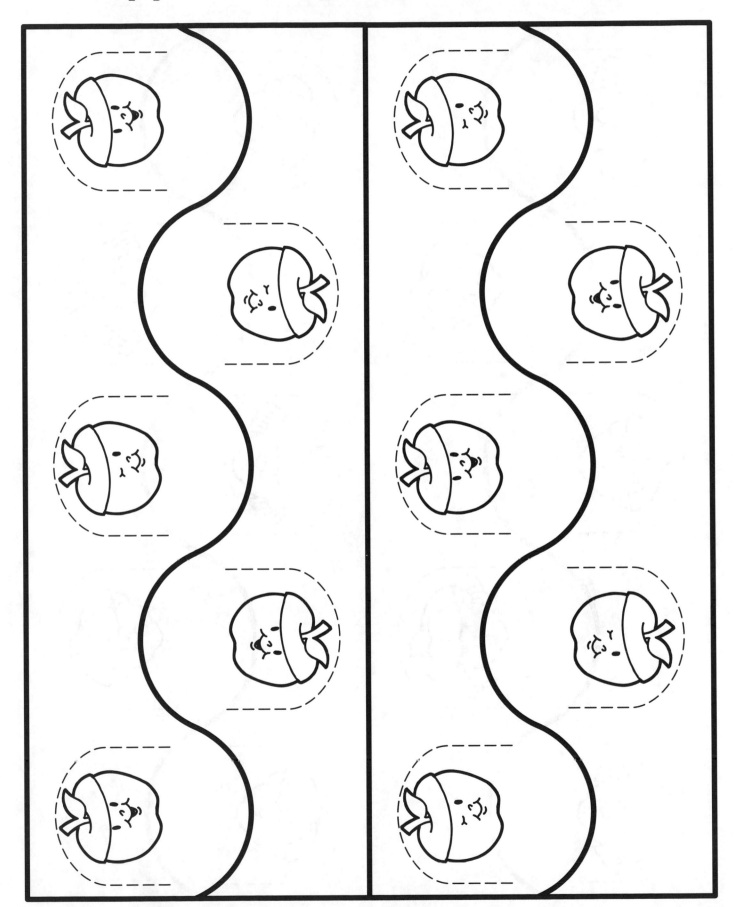

Pumpkin Patch Kids Pop-up Border

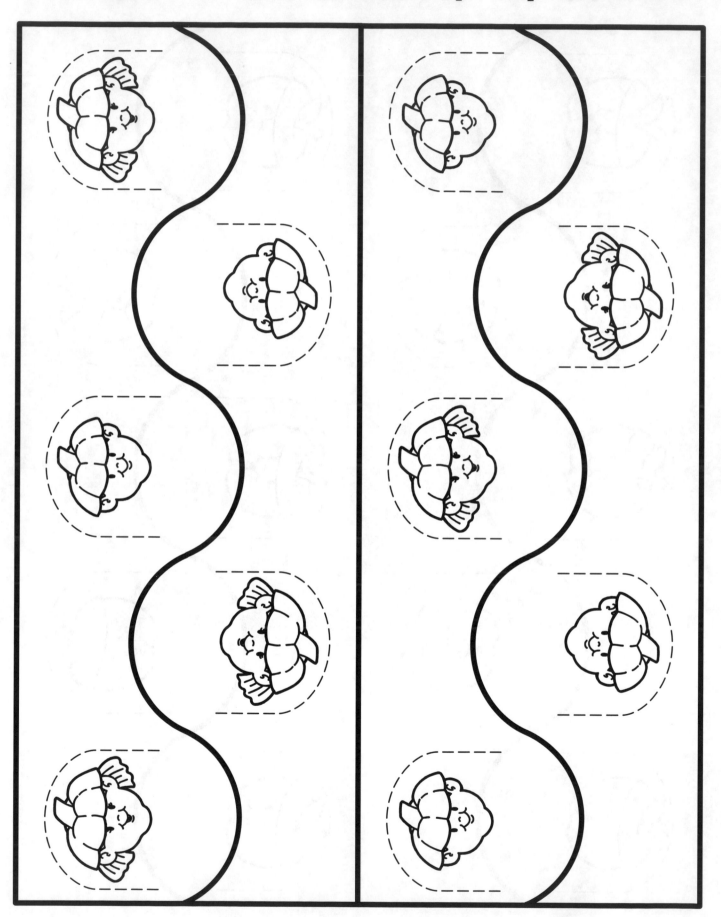

Professor Owl Pop-up Border

Farm Friends Pop-up Border

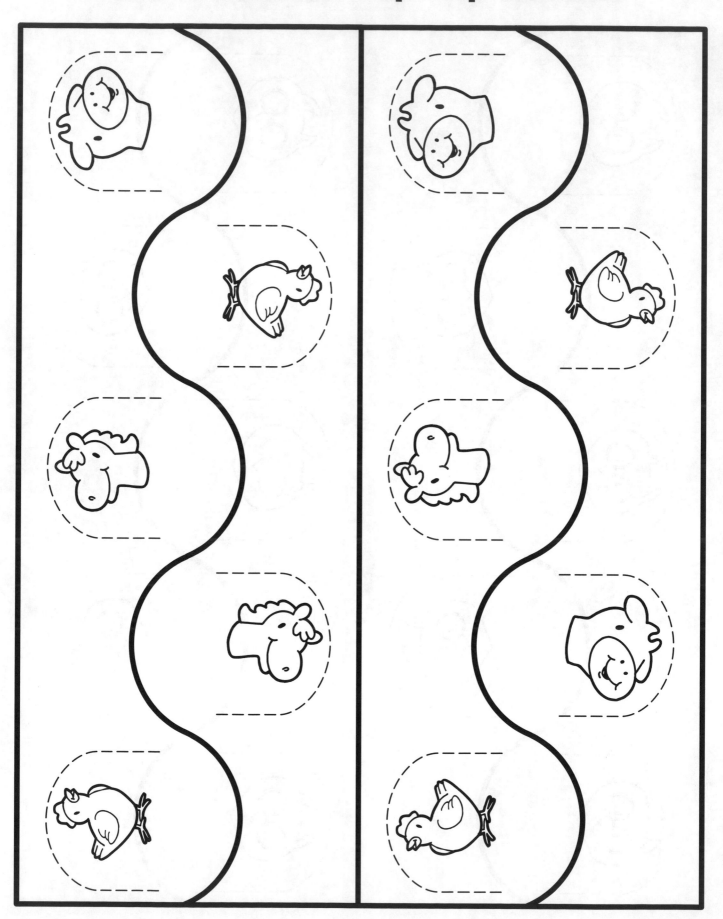

Apple Buddy Chart

Pumpkin Patch Kids Chart

Professor Owl Chart

Farm Friends Chart

Tags

Apple Buddy Spelling Word Pal

Pumpkin Patch Kids Spelling Word Pals

Professor Owl Spelling Word Pal

Farm Friends Spelling Word Pals

Labels

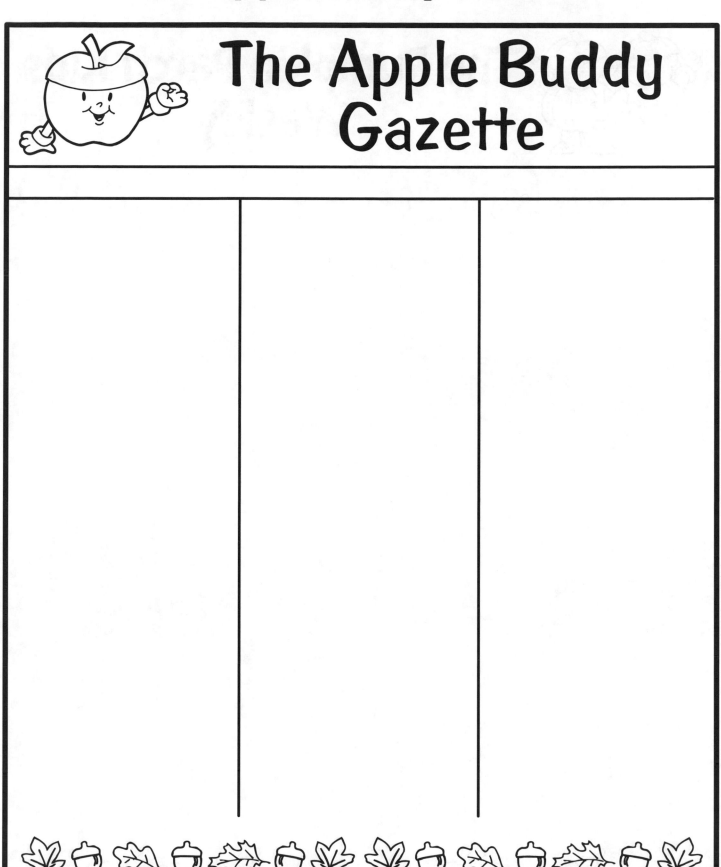

The Apple Buddy Gazette

The Pumpkin Patch Kids Weekly

Teacher Timesavers for Fall • ©2004 Monday Morning Books, Inc.

PROFESSOR OWL'S NEWS

Pencil Toppers

Book Ring Flash Cards

Apple Buddy Doorknob Hangers

Welcome!

Shhh!

Pumpkin Patch Kids Doorknob Hangers

Welcome!

Shhh!

Professor Owl Doorknob Hangers

Welcome!

Shhh!

Farm Friends Doorknob Hangers

Welcome!

Shhh!

Apple Buddy Counters

Pumpkin Patch Kids Counters

Teacher Timesavers for Fall • ©2004 Monday Morning Books, Inc.

Professor Owl Counters

Farm Friends Counters

Teacher Timesavers for Fall • ©2004 Monday Morning Books, Inc.

Apple Buddy Clock

Pumpkin Patch Kids Clock

Professor Owl Clock

Farm Friends Clock

Clock Hands

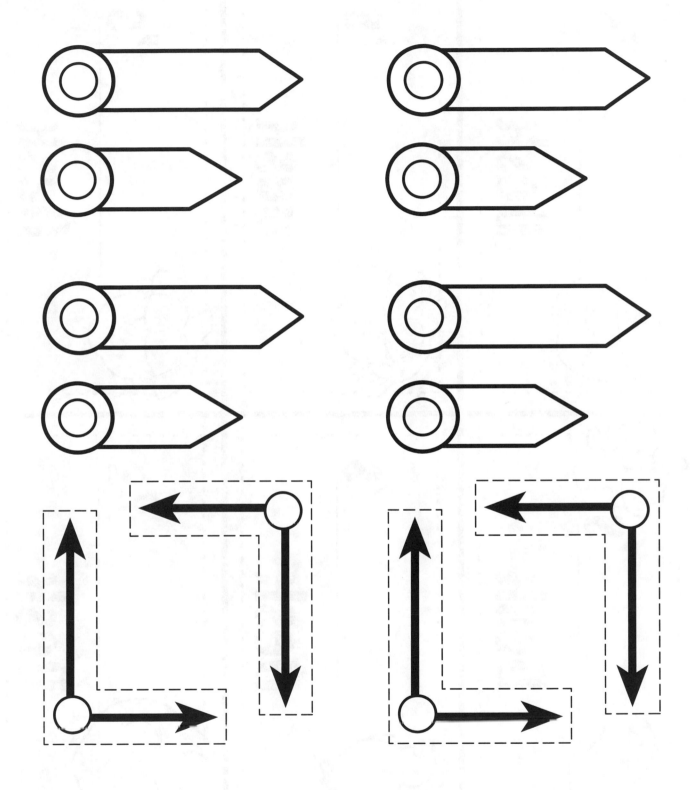

Desk Plates

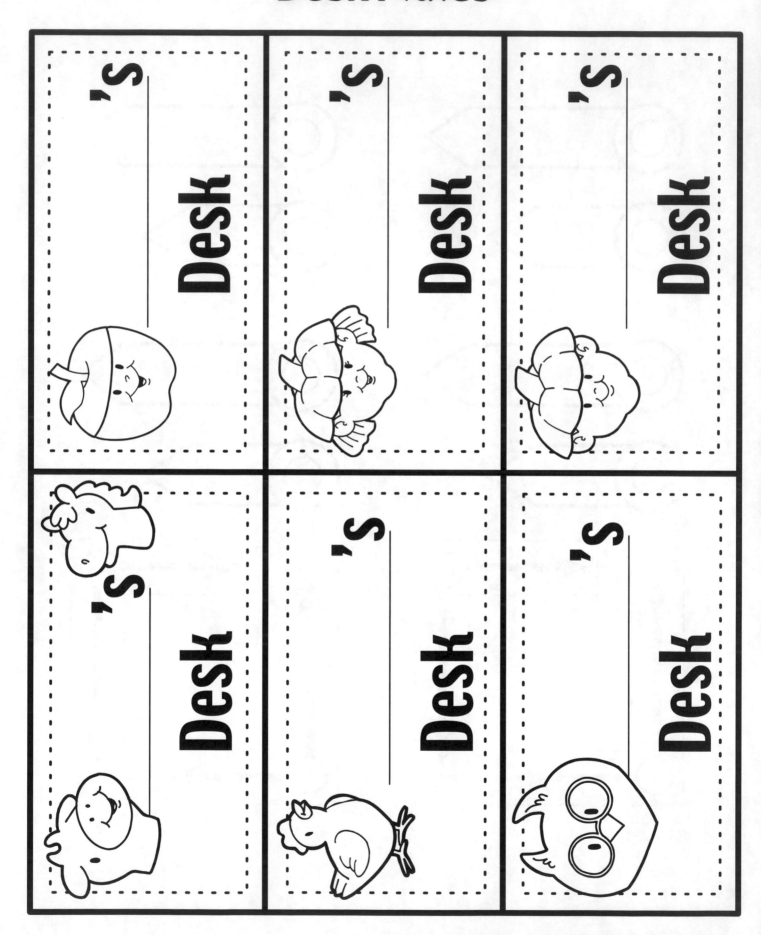

My Apple Buddy Book Report

by _____

My Pumpkin Patch Kids
Book Report

by _____

Professor Owl's Book Report Cover

Professor Owl's
Book Report

by _____

My Farm Friends Book Report

by _____

Bookmarks

Reading Feeds
Your Imagination

**Reading Is an
Adventure!**

Reading Is Fun!

Read a Little Every Day!

Book Plates

This Book Belongs To

This Book Belongs To

This Book Belongs To

This Book Belongs To

This Book Belongs To

This Book Belongs To

This Book Belongs To

This Book Belongs To

Math Awards

The Apple Buddy
MATH AWARD

To _____
For _____
Date _____
Signature _____

The Pumpkin Patch Kids
MATH AWARD

To _____
For _____
Date _____
Signature _____

The Farm Friends
MATH AWARD

To _____
For _____
Date _____
Signature _____

Professor Owl's
MATH AWARD

To _____
For _____
Date _____
Signature _____

Spelling Awards

The Apple Buddy
SPELLING AWARD

To _____
For _____
Date _____
Signature _____

The Pumpkin Patch Kids
SPELLING AWARD

To _____
For _____
Date _____
Signature _____

The Farm Friends
SPELLING AWARD

To _____
For _____
Date _____
Signature _____

Professor Owl's
SPELLING AWARD

To _____
For _____
Date _____
Signature _____

Science Awards

The Apple Buddy
SCIENCE AWARD

To _____
For _____
Date _____
Signature _____

The Pumpkin Patch Kids
SCIENCE AWARD

To _____
For _____
Date _____
Signature _____

The Farm Friends
SCIENCE AWARD

To _____
For _____
Date _____
Signature _____

Professor Owl's
SCIENCE AWARD

To _____
For _____
Date _____
Signature _____

Reading Awards

The Apple Buddy
READING AWARD

To _____
For _____
Date _____
Signature _____

The Pumpkin Patch Kids
READING AWARD

To _____
For _____
Date _____
Signature _____

The Farm Friends
READING AWARD

To _____
For _____
Date _____
Signature _____

Professor Owl's
READING AWARD

To _____
For _____
Date _____
Signature _____

Improved Awards

The Apple Buddy
IMPROVED AWARD

To _____
For _____
Date _____
Signature _____

The Pumpkin Patch Kids
IMPROVED AWARD

To _____
For _____
Date _____
Signature _____

The Farm Friends
IMPROVED AWARD

To _____
For _____
Date _____
Signature _____

Professor Owl's
IMPROVED AWARD

To _____
For _____
Date _____
Signature _____

Art Awards

The Apple Buddy
ART AWARD

To _____
For _____
Date _____
Signature _____

The Pumpkin Patch Kids
ART AWARD

To _____
For _____
Date _____
Signature _____

The Farm Friends
ART AWARD

To _____
For _____
Date _____
Signature _____

Professor Owl's
ART AWARD

To _____
For _____
Date _____
Signature _____

Credit Card Awards

CREDIT CARD AWARD **FIVE CREDITS**	CREDIT CARD AWARD **TEN CREDITS**
CREDIT CARD AWARD **FIVE CREDITS**	CREDIT CARD AWARD **TEN CREDITS**
CREDIT CARD AWARD **FIVE CREDITS**	CREDIT CARD AWARD **TEN CREDITS**
CREDIT CARD AWARD **FIVE CREDITS**	CREDIT CARD AWARD **TEN CREDITS**

Achievement Awards

The Apple Buddy
ACHIEVEMENT AWARD

To _____

For _____

Date _____

Signature _____

The Pumpkin Patch Kids
ACHIEVEMENT AWARD

To _____

For _____

Date _____

Signature _____

The Farm Friends
ACHIEVEMENT AWARD

To _____

For _____

Date _____

Signature _____

Professor Owl's
ACHIEVEMENT AWARD

To _____

For _____

Date _____

Signature _____